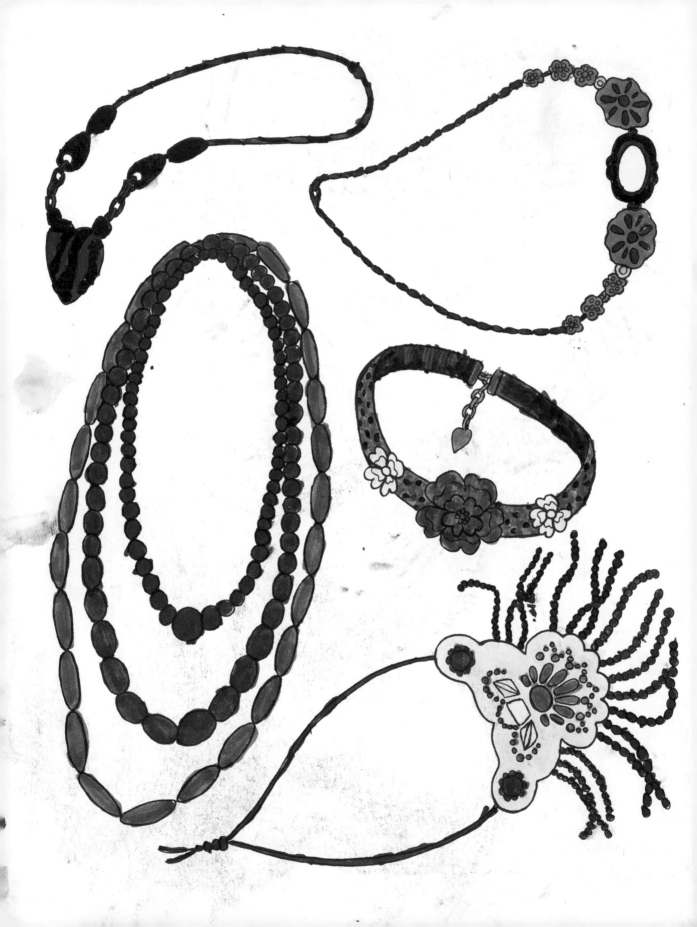

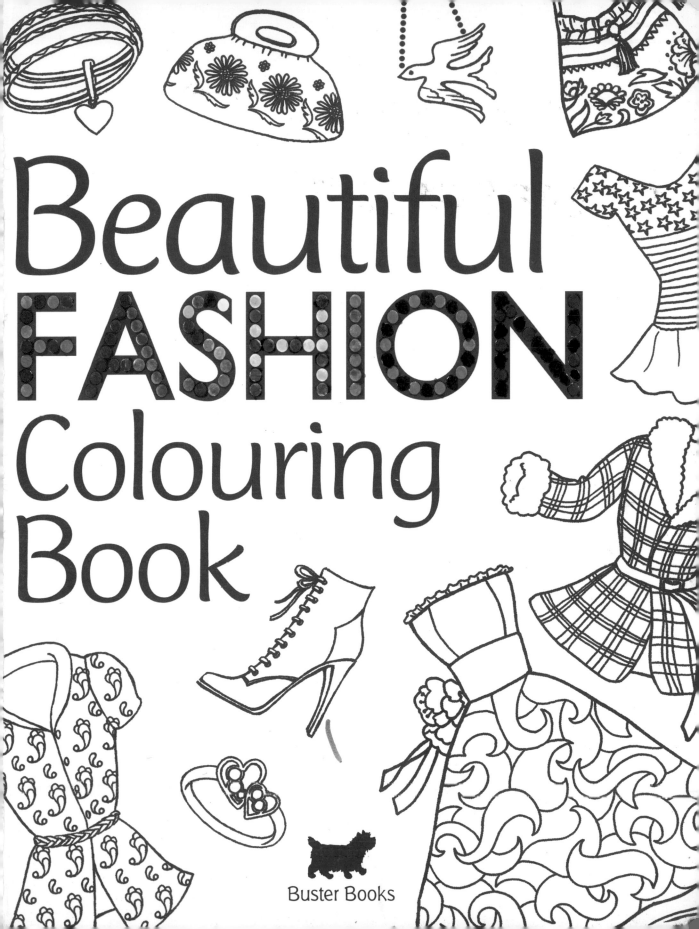

Beautiful
FASHION
Colouring
Book

Buster Books

Illustrated by Katy Jackson

First published in Great Britain in 2011 by Buster Books,
an imprint of Michael O'Mara Books Limited,
9 Lion Yard, Tremadoc Road, London SW4 7NQ

www.mombooks.com/busterbooks

Copyright © Buster Books 2011
Cover design by Angie Allison

A CIP catalogue record for this book is available from the British Library.

ISBN: 978-1-907151-55-2

2 4 6 8 10 9 7 5 3 1

This book was printed in February 2011 by L.E.G.O., Viale dell'Industria 2, 36100, Vicenza, Italy.

Papers used by Buster Books are natural, recyclable products
made from wood grown in sustainable forests. The manufacturing processes
conform to the environmental regulations of the country of origin.

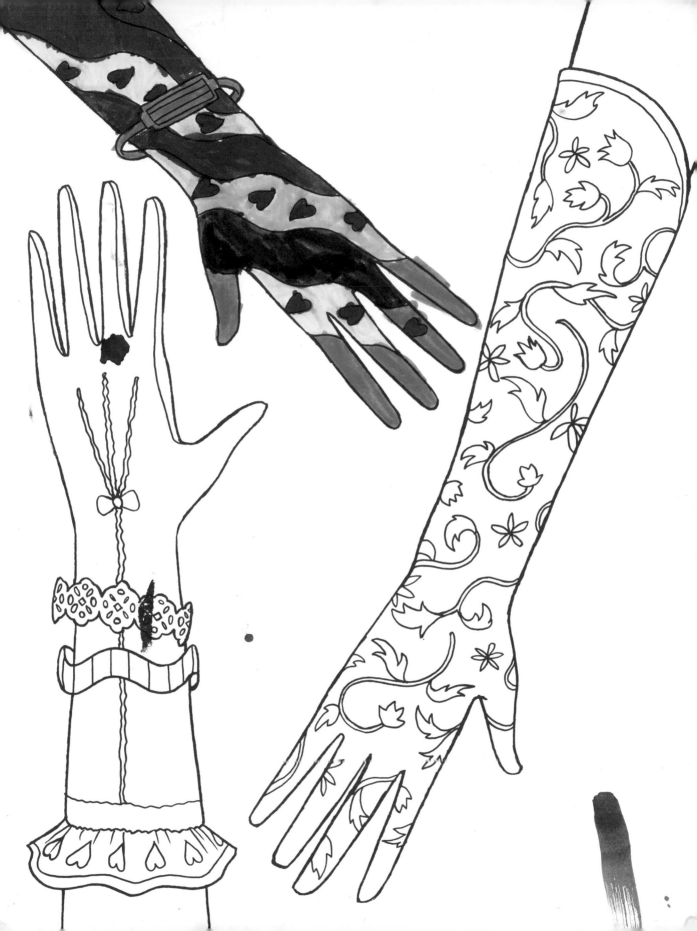

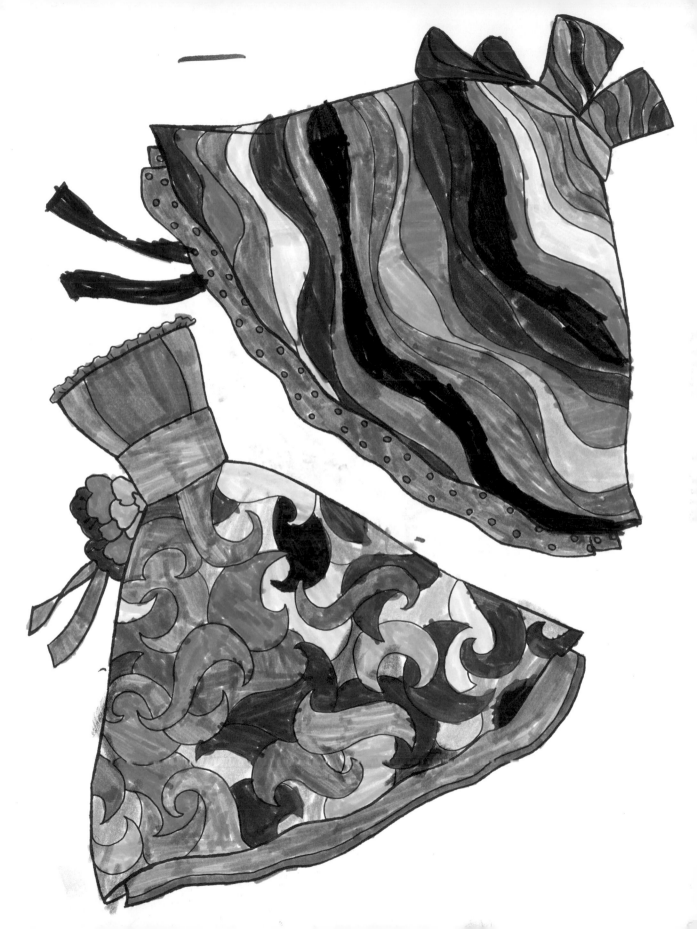

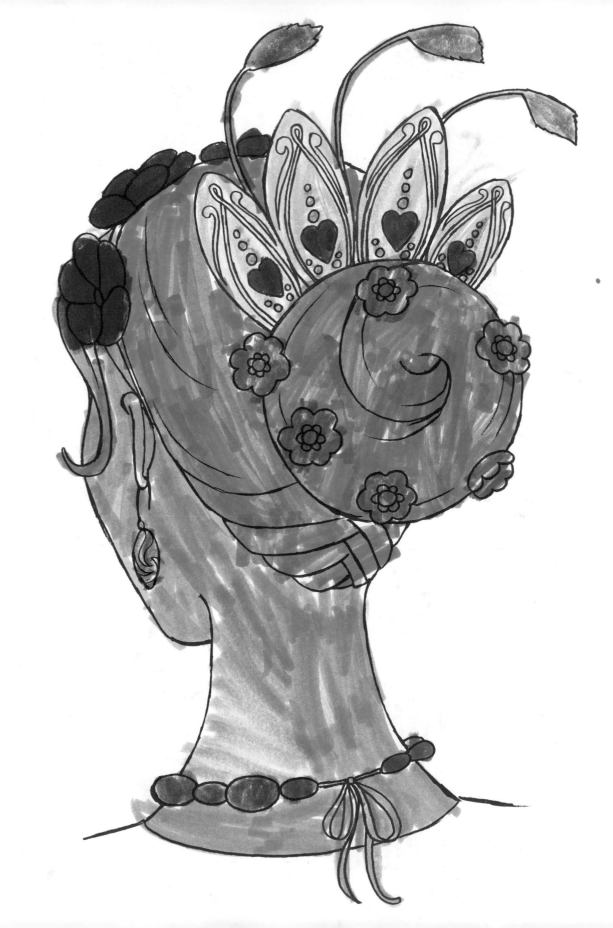

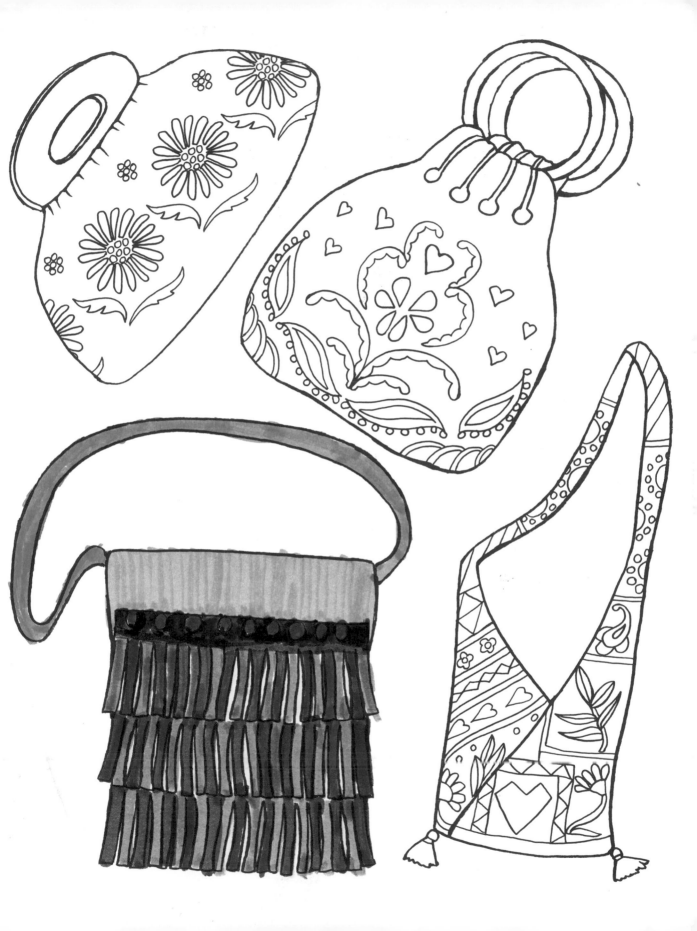

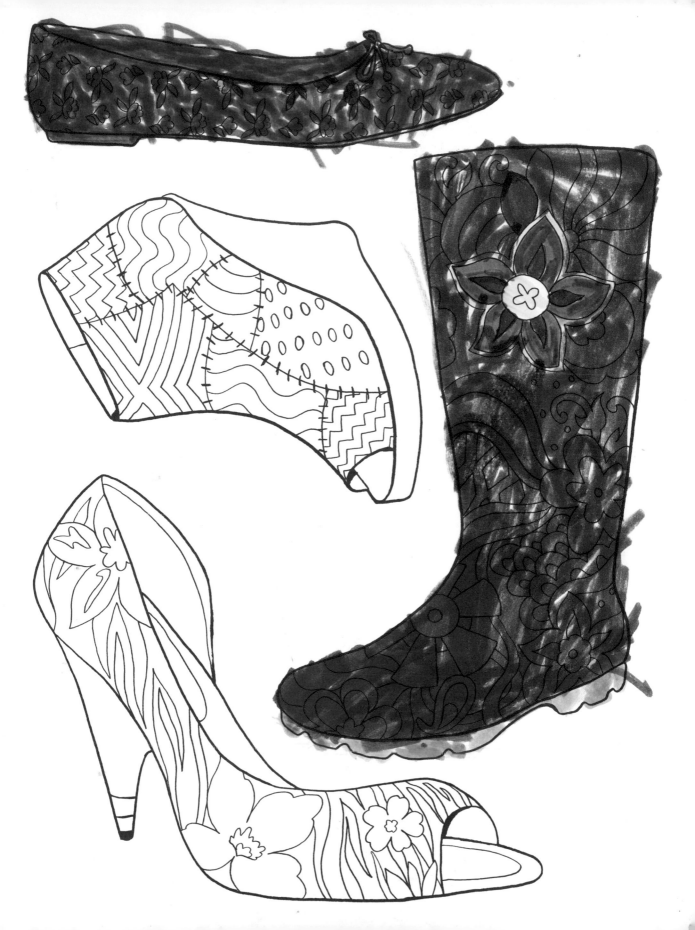

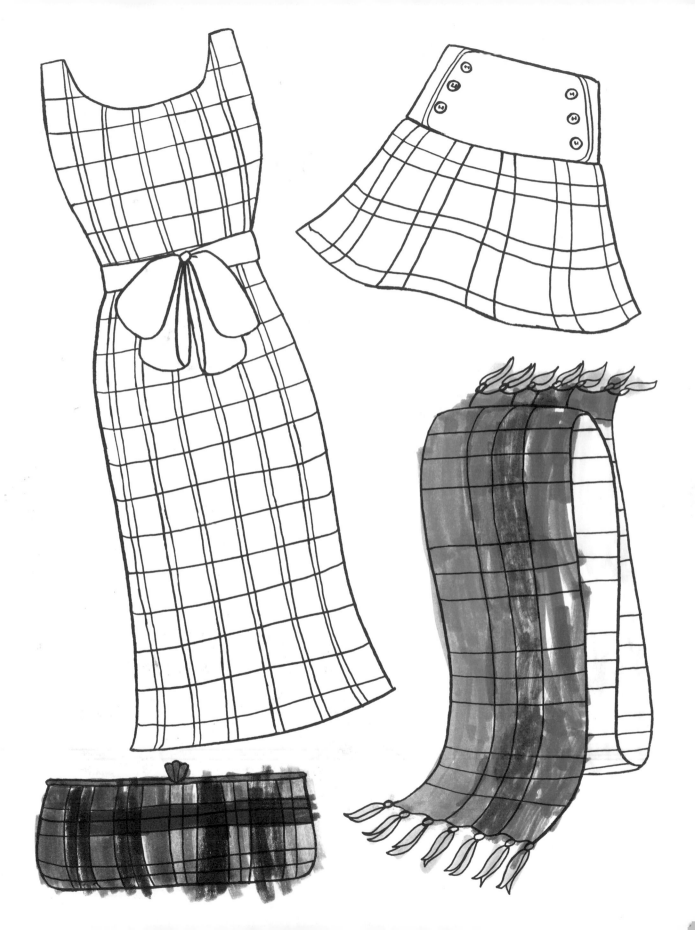

Tiger

Tiger DrEss

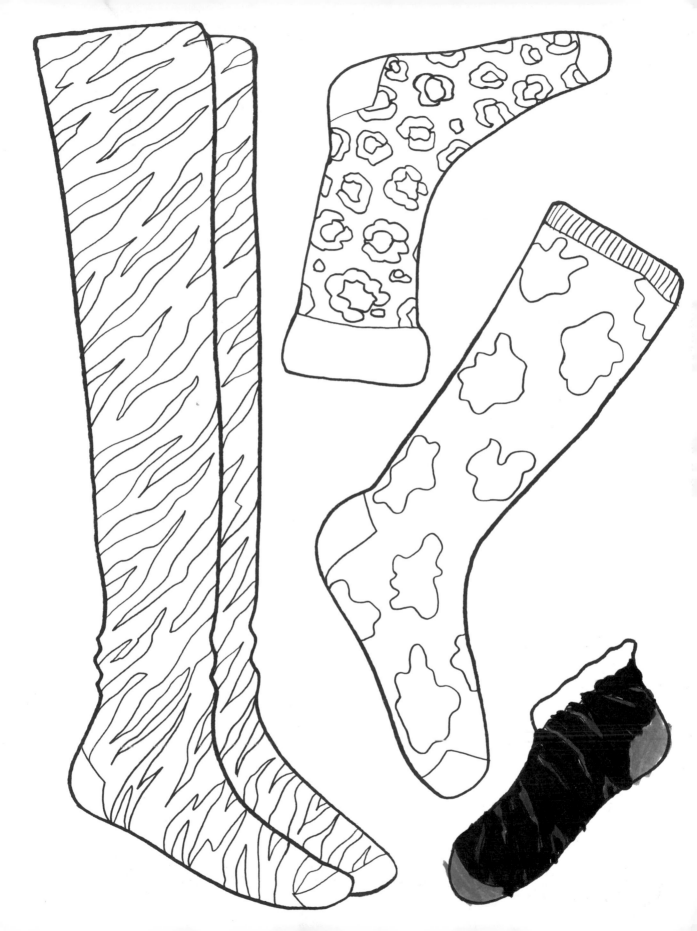

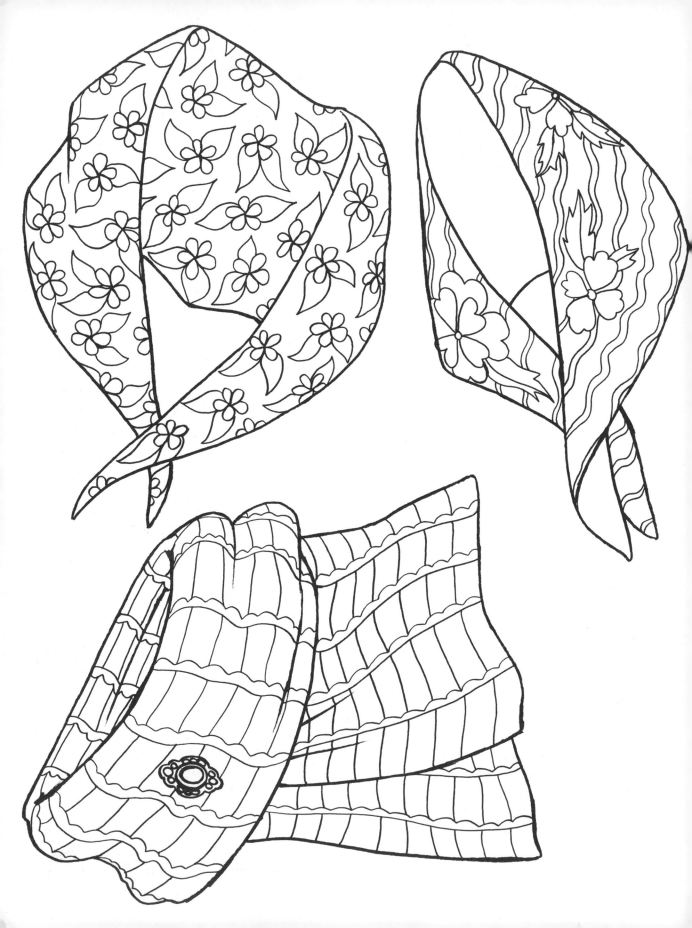

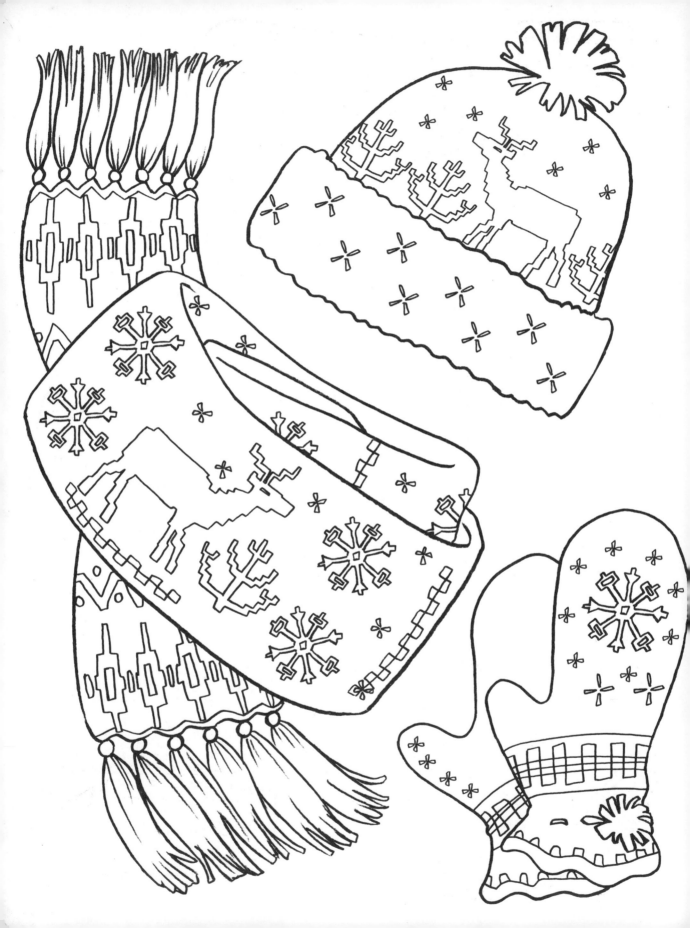